Dear Sir Anthony

DEAR SIR ANTHONY

Unrequited Mail

Anne Loudon
Cartoons by
Patricia Drennan

Stanley Paul
London   Melbourne   Auckland   Johannesburg

Stanley Paul & Co. Ltd

An imprint of Century Hutchinson Ltd

62–65 Chandos Place, London WC2N 4NW

Century Hutchinson Australia (Pty) Ltd
PO Box 496, 16–22 Church Street, Hawthorn, Melbourne, Victoria 3122

Century Hutchinson New Zealand Ltd
PO Box 40-086, Glenfield, Auckland 10

Century Hutchinson South Africa (Pty) Ltd
PO Box 337, Bergvlei 2012, South Africa

First published 1987

© Anne Loudon 1987

Set in 11/12 pt Linotron Plantin by
Rowland Phototypesetting Ltd
Bury St Edmunds, Suffolk

Printed and bound in Great Britain by
Anchor Brendon Ltd, Tiptree, Essex

British Library Cataloguing in Publication Data
Loudon, Anne
  Dear Sir Anthony: unrequited mail.
  I. Title
  828'.91407   PN6175
  ISBN 0 09 172662 X

Family letter-writers to Sir Anthony Haslemere, Bt.
The Hon. Arthur Alton, his uncle (his mother's younger
    brother)
Lady Caroline Barker, his first wife, remarried, mother of his
    daughters
Madame Givusakiz (Yasmin), his French/Iranian fiancée
Parviz and Fatima Givusakiz, his stepchildren
Charles and Warren Haslemere, his twin sons by Witney
Claire Haslemere, his younger daughter
Drucilla Haslemere, his elder daughter
Geoffrey Haslemere, his younger brother
Primrose, Lady Haslemere, his elderly widowed mother
Mrs Haslemere (Witney), his second wife, American and
    mother of the twins
The Hon. Mrs Hackentry (his Aunt Violet)
Lord Petersfield, his Uncle Ivor (his mother's elder brother)

Other letter-writers
Dr Bettah from the RECUPA Medical Centre
Mr Bull, his stockbroker – of Caper, Cures & Mine
Fred Chudd, his fishing adviser
R. U. Crumlin, dry-rot specialist
Jack Finch, his publisher – of Gassing & Phartus
Derek Force, his solicitor – of Blathers & Co.
Mr and Mrs David Goldstein (David and Annabel), his
    literary agent and wife
Lord and Lady Hampshire (Charles and Fiona), friends
Dr Henderson, his GP
Mrs Kettle, his cook/housekeeper
Marquesa Fernando Malventura (Eliza), his one-time Italian
    mistress
'Mior', a Paris couturier
Monsieur Omosesuele, the manager of the Hotel Piszt
Sultan Ahbed Soluvly, an Arab
Mr Teak, his sons' housemaster
Rupert Tiddlesworth, a friend of Drucilla
Harry Till, the manager of Hoares Bank
Edward West, estate surveyor

This extraordinary new machine

The Old Rectory
Wet Waltham
Near Rottingdean
Sussex

5 February

Anthony darling,

Is this wise? Your father would turn in his grave. You know how he felt about coloured people.

I know you told me about this glamorous lady you met abroad in the summer, but I had no idea you were serious, let alone contemplating marriage.

What does Caroline think? And Drucilla and Claire? Have they met her? And what about the twins, with that vulgar mother of theirs such miles away?

Please take my advice, darling, and think before you make another error. I'll be coming to London shortly. We'll talk about it then.

I had a letter from Charles and Warren enclosing a photograph of you all during the Xmas holidays. Goodness they do remind me of you at that age, so blond and tall for fifteen. (It is fifteen, isn't it?) They seem to be settling down better this term and even doing some work. I'm glad their manners have improved.

This frost is playing havoc with the garden and I'm very worried about the roses.

I can't ring you as British Telecom have installed this extraordinary new machine here with buttons, and I don't understand how to work it.

Uncle Arthur came for the weekend. He has put on masses of weight and was smoking and coughing a lot. I've heard he's taken to the bottle but I don't think that can be true as he's always so very thirsty in the mornings.

This cold spell seems never-ending and it is not doing my arthritis any good, but one mustn't complain. When I read in the newspapers about so many people of my age dying of hypothermia it makes one wonder. Why don't they install central heating? My new oil system works very well and keeps me warm as toast.

Aunt Vi keeps writing and suggests that it would do me good to stay with her. It is quite cold enough here without going all the way to Alaska. I suppose those huge dogs she breeds keep her warm.

To go back to your intended nuptials, please ponder my advice carefully.

I hope to see you soon. Perhaps we could have lunch with Uncle Arthur one day?

Your loving mother,
Primrose

PS: Any news from Uncle Ivor, darling? I usually get a Christmas card, but this year not a word. I wonder where he's gone now?

Blathers & Co
Gray's Inn
London WC1

5 February

Dear Anthony,

I was somewhat surprised to hear that you are thinking
of marrying yet again and feel that, as your legal adviser,
I should point out the financial implications of this move.

The alimony you pay your two ex-wives, coupled with
the twins' school fees, dig a large hole in your pocket as it is.
You give generous allowances to your daughters, Drucilla
and Claire, and a covenant to your mother, Lady Primrose.
A new and possibly extravagant young bride could cause
financial embarrassment in the foreseeable future.

In the past your bestselling thrillers brought in substantial
royalties, but since you changed your style of writing your
earned income seems to have dwindled to very modest
amounts indeed.

Lady Caroline's solicitor is an old friend of mine, and on
that side all is amicable. I only wish I could say the same
of the American lawyer representing your second wife, from
whom I receive vitriolic pages regularly once a month.

I wish you all the best, but please do not hesitate to consult
me at any time. That is what I am here for.

Yours ever,
Derek

Hock Hall
Hove

5 February

My dear Tony,

I spied in my *Times* this morning your engagement to
what sounds like a 'Madmoiselle'? Congratulations, or
should I say commiserations! Third time lucky, what?

As you know I prefer to dabble here and there rather than
risk tying the knot. Our dear mama doesn't approve.

By the way, old boy, do you remember that sultry beauty
I had a walk out with back in the sixties . . . daughter of
the Chilean Ambassador? Her husband has become
entangled with the vine as well, so we had that in common
too! Didn't realize the Chileans knew so many tricks of the
trade. They've lent me a pad south of Santiago on a river
where they have the best fishing in the world. We ought to
go and cast a fly or two there.

Well, all the best old man,
Geoffrey

PS: Got a bit stuck on the crossword this morning, bottom
right corner. That's why I flicked to the engagement page.
Did you finish it?

Give me a ring. Your line's permanently engaged.

Foxhole Farm
Lower Downe
Sodbury
Wiltshire

6 February

Dear Tony

I suppose I should congratulate you, but – another foreigner? Are you crazy or still over-sexed? Or is it because the ego needs another boost with the new books not selling? I hope the girls approve. Drucilla seems even scattier than usual and Claire has been in Bali *far* too long. Can't you do something about it? It's always me that has to nag; my poor Cecil is so patient but he's no spring chicken now and getting awfully deaf. Your twins may tend to take priority, but the girls are yours too, you know – even though they've been spared your long nose and have failed to grow to the height of the Post Office Tower.

Will we have the pleasure of meeting your new 'Madame' one day or are you going to keep her to yourself?

Well, good luck, anyway. Give me a ring.

Love,
Caroline

24 Louisburg Square
Beacon Hill
Boston
Mass

6 February

Shitface,

What's all this crap about you getting married to a wog/
frog? You already have an Italian bit on the side. OK, Tex
fucked off to LA, but what are *you* trying to achieve? An
even Commoner Market?

Boston society is horrified and you have made me the
laughing stock of the city. How could you be such a
bastard? Have you thought of Charles and Warren in that
prison you insist on them attending? What do they think?

I'm off to Lyford Cay to stay with the Richies. Then I
might take the boys out for half-term, just for the hell of
it.

Witney

PS: I suppose the blackie was taken in by your fair looks
and watery blue eyes. Or perhaps she fancied your new
title? Boy, wait till she has to read all that trash you write.

Gassing & Phartus Ltd
32 Craven Street
London W2

6 February

Dear Sir Anthony,

We were sorry to hear that your American publishers Triplenight have gone into liquidation, a few days, I believe, after sending us a finished copy of the US edition of your book, *Wildfowl in Peking: Communism and the Environment.* As requested we shall of course reconsider the book for the UK market; however you will appreciate that we did assess the original manuscript most carefully before advising your literary agent, Mr David Goldstein, that we couldn't make a publishing offer. The market will not bear too many socio-politico-environmental studies, however painstakingly written.

Yours sincerely,
Jack Finch

The Intercontinental Hotel
Teheran
Iran

3 February

Chéri,

Je t'adore. Teheran is not the same without you. Teheran
is not the same at all. I lose everything. My home, my
family, my friends and my diamonds. But I have you, my
one and only jewel. I die to be with you again, to feel your
hands on my body making me come alive.

It was beautiful in Monaco last September, no? You
change my life. I wait with joy to meet your little ones,
your old mama and all other friends.

My husband, Reza, he is being very Iranian and difficult
about the divorce. I know I also half Persian, but I feel so
much more the French half. I stay with Papa in Paris on my
return to you. There I will chose my wedding outfit and
some très sexy lingerie to tempt you, mon amour.

I also will visit a sweet little curé I know who maybe I
persuade (he has a very poor church) to forget all other
mistakes and marry us in March. Yes?

Many kisses all over you. How is going the writing?

Your
Yasmin

PS: I meet a nice Italian here, he go to London tonight and
bring letter. Is more quick, no?

le petit trousseau to tempt

Box 2242
Running Dog Rapids
Juneau
Alaska

20 January

Primmy dearest,

It is high time you came to visit me here, and I really think it would do you the power of good. You write about gardening, greenhouses and grandchildren and here am I, fourteen years older than you (in dog years), trekking the mountainside every day and cleaning kennels, and I've never felt better. Mind you, I suppose I was always made of sterner stuff, Prim! You'd *never* have stood up to the parents and eloped with a GI, your wartime sweetheart. Teddy may only have been a lumberjack, bless him, but our high and mighty Lord and Lady Petersfield would have had to swallow some of their own medicine if they had seen the miles of forest he moved just before he died.

I liked the photograph you sent me of Anthony and his children. Was that you in the background? You've got much too thin. Gracious me, those twins look just like their father when he was a puppy. I feel out of touch here, with no telephone or wireless. I must invite them all to stay. The young would have fun sledding and snowballing, and Anthony could try skiing, any time of the year. We are not far from the glacier, and I have been busy training the Newfoundlands to pull the sleighs.

Please write soon.

Much love,
Violet

We are not far from the glacier

Veld & Leikt
1 Bedford Street
London W1

7 February

Darling Daddy,

Congratulations! Mummy says you've finally come to your senses and ditched that American cow for good and all. What's the new bird like? Does she speak English? Mummy said she's abroad. Please ring me when she's back. Witney was all right, but I feel sorry for the boys, as she clearly doesn't give a damn about them. I mean, swanning around the Bahamas all winter with those ghastly mega-millionaires, discussing face-lifts and every other sort of lift, just to keep tanning that leathery old skin. She may not think it, but she looks much older than Mummy really.

I take Charlie and Warren out to tea sometimes at weekends and I tell you they are up to no good there. Lucky buggers, being identical!

Forgive typed letter but I'm in the office about to get the sack if I use the phone (sorry, telephone!) any more.

Masses of love,
Drucilla

PS: I'll ring from the flat one evening to hear the latest.

swanning around the Bahamas

Veld & Leikt
1 Bedford Street
London W1

7 February

Dear long-lost sister!

Finally I'm coming to see you. You've been away for
bloody ages, and I feel as if I haven't had a holiday in months.
Anyway I've bought a ticket halfway and put a huge deposit
on a jeep or something to drive the rest, so I can see a bit
of Malaysia, Singapore, or whatever. It cost an arm and a
leg but that was my worry and is all dealt with.

I suppose you've heard from Mummy that Daddy's going
to marry a girl only five years older than me? What can
she see in him? He may think he's frightfully trendy, but
he's getting on a bit now really. I'm hoping to meet her
soon. I'll let you know what she's like when I see you.

You are lucky being in a decent climate. It's colder than
a witch's tit here and has been for the past month or more.

Great Aunt Violet keeps inviting all of us to stay with her
in Newfoundland or some godforsaken place. Mummy's
fine. Busy shouting at old Cecil, walking the dogs, exercising
the horses and worrying about you.

My job gets more boring every day but I've spent some
quite jolly weekends in the country.

Fingers crossed that this girl is an improvement on the
dreaded Witney.

Longing to see you.

Tons of love,
Dru

Hotel Piszt
Place Vendôme
Paris

5 February

Dear Sir,

I confirm with pleasure your reservation for the Bridal
Suite at the Piszt Hotel on 16 March for a week.

A certain number of packages have been delivered here
for your future wife, which I will store safely for her pending
your arrival.

We look forward to seeing you and hope your stay will be
a pleasant one.

Yours faithfully,
M. N. Omosesuele

69 Laxford House
Cundy Street
London SW1

8 February

Carissimo,

Non lo credo! I hear you marry quella stronza. Is true?
You cannot do this to me so sudden after all those beautiful
times we spent together. Never will I forget that first night
in your funny little bed when Fernando went to Teheran on
business, or that weekend in that horrible hotel in Cornwall.
It was wet and cold but wonderful excuse to stay all the
day in the bed.

Venice was a peccato, but how I know we find Marino
and Lucia? Now Fernando so mad at me you cannot even
ring here, and I not dare to call you. Please, amore, tell me
what I am hearing is just gossip of naughty-minded people.

I am *waiting, waiting* for your letter.

I kiss you, I love you, but I hate you.

Your desperate
Eliza

Hoare's Bank
33 Fleet Street
London EC4

8 February

Dear Sir,

With regard to your request to be kept informed: your eldest daughter Drucilla's overdraft stands at £2225 to date, a large increase from last month's £200. I have written to her accordingly, suggesting that she repays in instalments, plus some interest. It is rather an exorbitant amount, I am sorry to say. Has she just bought a new car?

Yours truly,
Harry Till

Sloane's
Slough

9 February

Hi Pop,

This dump isn't so bad after all. We're making out OK this term and things are looking up. We've figured out the study programme, classes, homework, etc., much better.

The food has improved too. Mr Teak says he put on weight in the Xmas vacation so now we don't have so much British stodge or French fries.

Hey? – Mom wrote that you are getting hitched up to a new broad. Is it true? Hope she'll come take us out for a decent steak sometime soon. Xmas was great and we are just crazy waiting to try out the new skis. Thanks, Pop. Terrific gifts. Have a nice day!

> Love and stuff,
> *Charlie or Warren?*

Sloane's
Slough

10 February

Dear Druci,

Please come down soon. We want to know all about our wicked stepmother! Dad seemed kinda old and vague last vacation. What's with him marrying again? Surely people of that age are past sex?

We are getting to grips with this place slowly and think maybe we can make it after all.

Write soon. It's no good calling. The line's always busy.

Love,
Charlie and Warren

PS: Sorry about throwing up all over your bathroom floor.

Poste Restante
PO Box IM12
Bali
Indonesia

24 January

Dearest Father

   I received a telegram from my mother to tell me that you
are acquiring another wife. I have joined a commune here
that believes in many wives, or 'partners' as they call them
in the 'frangipani' sect, so I am very happy for you. Poppy,
Dogrose, Frank, Pansy, Bull, Xaviour and Rosie all join me
in wishing you happiness in your new union.
   My sister has written to tell me that she has booked a
flight to Bahrain and is planning to rent a Land-Rover to
drive here to see me. I am a little concerned about this as I
do not think she will like our life-style very much, and
will not fit in with the crowd here at all. Please try and
dissuade her.
   Many blessings be showered upon you.

                    Your daughter,
                    Claire

Bali high

The Beach
Cobblers Cove
Barbados

25 January

Dear old Prim,

So life is grim, your letters state from day to day ever
since I've been away. Arthur sometimes writes his news,
his racing views, his drinking blues, it makes me snooze.
Do I reply? Why?

Does no one care, how I fare? Your favourite son, dropped
a line, to say's he's fine. Got a new bird, I heard.

Here my life is utter bliss, there's not a soul I really miss.
Invited all of you to stay but not a word . . . not yea or
nay.

Happy New Year, old dear.

Ivor

28

Beechers Lodge
Portishall
Near Newbury
Berkshire

12 February

My dear boy,

Primmy tells me that you are about to back another filly.
How many is that now? I've rather lost count. She seemed
a little distraught (your mother, I mean).

I didn't have anything against Caroline, old chap, but not
much time for Witney.

I'll be at the club on Tuesday at noon, if you have a
moment.

I was sorry to have missed you at Newbury. Apart from
the biting wind, had rather a good day. O'Manahan's tips
came in for a change, and I had a bit of luck.

All the best, dear boy,
Uncle Arthur

PS: Perhaps you should invite yourself to spend your
honeymoon with my drop-out brother, your Uncle Ivor.
His desert island sounds idyllic, if you like that sort of
thing.

The Old Rectory
Wet Waltham
Near Rottingdean
Sussex

12 February

Dearest Arthur

Could you possibly give me a lift to London next week?
It's not that much out of your way and good old Baxter is
down with a particularly virulent flu. I don't remember the
name of this year's virus – Asian, I expect. Maybe the
Government should stop all these immigrants from the Far
East. We could discuss Anthony's intended marriage in
the car. It worries me a lot. The boy may be an excellent
shot, good golfer, first-class angler, keen punter, avid skier
and fair bridge-player, but he has never earned a penny. (I
don't count this ridiculous writing business.) I can only
pray that the new one will be an improvement on that
dreadful American.

Drop me a postcard if you can give me a lift. I can't hear
the telephone.

All love, darling.
Primrose

PS: I had a letter from Ivor written entirely in verse. I fear
he has gone round the bend, and Vi is now threatening
to ship me one of her confounded dogs.

Hoare's Bank
33 Fleet Street
London EC4

20 February

Dear Sir Anthony,

I am pleased to inform you that your daughter Drucilla
has remitted sufficient monies to cover her overdraft of
£2225. I was somewhat surprised to receive the entire sum
in cash.

Please do not hesitate to let us know if you will be wanting
to open a separate account for the future Lady Haslemere?

Yours truly,
Harry Till

Gassing & Phartus Ltd
32 Craven Street
London W2

23 February

Dear Sir Anthony,

Thank you for sending us yet another copy of the American edition of *Wildfowl in Peking: Communism and the Environment*. While we hold Mr David Goldstein, your literary agent, in the highest possible regard, we cannot finally reverse our original decision and make you a publishing offer.

As the detective stories you wrote were such a great success, particularly the series starring 'The White Elephant' or 'The Black Sheep . . .' might it not be possible to continue in your fictional vein? This could regain your old readership.

Yours faithfully,
Jack Finch

Claridges Hotel
Brook Street
London W1

26 February

Most Honourable Sir,

I recently spent a most satisfactory, splendiferous, exotic and pleasurable night of love with your daughter, in exchange for a small sum, in my suite here in Claridges, and I am writing to ask for her hand in marriage. She will be well cared for as I own many dollars, many many acres of desert, and plenty palaces, Cadillacs, camels, etc.

I also have sixteen wives and ninety-two children, so she will never be lonely. With most eager anticipation I await your answer.

Yours most humbly,
Ahbed Soluvly

The Finn
Much Slaughter
Trialbridge
Dorset

25 February

Dear Sir Anthony,

   The fishing season is approaching and I wondered if you
wished to take your usual rod on the River Scratch? We
are hoping for a bonanza year due to the heavy rain this
autumn. A right perishing winter to boot, which bodes
well for the rainbows and brownies. The little slipperers are
easily tickled to death by a bit of warm sun rippling on
the water after the bitter cold, and rise like fish (if you'll
excuse the pun).
   I look forward to hearing from you.

                    Yours sincerely,
                    Fred Chudd

PS: We much enjoyed having your American friends with
    us in September and so hope they will be coming again this
    year. Perhaps, if you happen to talk to them, you could
    tactfully suggest that, with clothing of a more muted
    hue, they might have better luck.

The Old Rectory
Wet Waltham
Near Rottingdean
Sussex

26 February

Anthony darling,

I'm afraid I can't even hear the new telephone ring, let alone use it. It makes a funny squeaking noise which can only be detected if you are literally on top of it.

Poor Uncle Arthur had a stroke at Lingfield yesterday afternoon and was rushed to Prince Henry's, so I'll be going up to London this week again to visit him.

I ran into Annabel Goldstein in the Peter Jones China Department last week, and she told me that your fiancée has also been married before and has two teenagers, although she is only twenty-nine. I suppose these kind of foreigners do tend to marry awfully young.

Annabel said you'd been up to Hampstead to talk to David about a new book. What are you writing about now, darling? I'm afraid your last book was way above my head. I wish you'd go back to the 'whodunnits'. I enjoyed those, although I never guessed who'd done it.

I'm going across to Rosemary's for a rubber of bridge tonight so I'll ring you from there with news of Arthur. I much look forward to coming to dinner next week. Would you come with me to visit him that afternoon?

Your loving mother

The RECUPA Medical Centre
229 Graves Inn Road
London WC1

26 February

Dear Sir Anthony,

I have sent the results of your recent medical tests here directly to your GP as I feel it is best that you discuss them with him personally.

Yours sincerely,
Michael Bettah FRCS

Hock Hall
Hove

26 February

My dear Tony,

Just back from Santiago to get your message about dinner.
Love to come, old boy. I decided to have a butcher's at
this river in Chile, on my way to the vineyards. It's an
angler's paradise, a real challenge even for us pros. Let's
give it a whirl in the near future. Your new wife would fit
in well with the local talent, too. Much the same colouring
and temperament, I'd say!
Think about it. Look forward to seeing you next week,
and the meeting with 'La belle France'.

Yours,
Geoffrey

Foxhole Farm
Lower Downe
Sodbury
Wiltshire

6 March

Darling Tony,

It was thoughtful of you to invite Cecil and me to dinner
to meet your new fiancée. She seemed quite pleasant really,
under all that heavy make-up, false eye-lashes and blue-black
hair, but I can't see her getting on very well with the girls.
She kept looking daggers at Drucilla, and even docile old
Fred had his hackles up.

I had a word with Mrs Kettle to congratulate her on the
dinner. I think you had better tread carefully there.
Foreigners are not very sensitive with staff although if Mrs
Kettle survived Witney she'll survive anything.

I had a long chat with your mother and those ghastly
Hampshires (actually I suppose he's not that bad), and it
was nice to see Geoffrey, looking as dapper as ever.

Drucilla says she's getting on all right with her job but in
the same breath tells me she is planning a trip abroad.
There was a ridiculous rumour going around Wiltshire that
she had been spotted with an Arab, in full traditional
dress, in the foyer of some London hotel. Really, some
people will believe anything!!

Claire's life in Bali worries me a lot. She sounds so
different in her letters recently. Could she be on drugs or
something equally ghastly?

One of the puppies ate Cecil's monogrammed slippers.
Please ring me.

Love and thanks again,
Caroline

spotted with an Arab in full traditional dress

'Mior'
Rue St Benedict
Paris VIIeme

1 March

Most Honourable Sir,

Madame Givusakiz asked me to send you the account for her trousseau. I am herewith enclosing l'addition for 500,000 francs and await your prompt payment.

Madame, who is an old and valued client of ours, tells me that she is engaged to your lordship. I look forward to the pleasure of making your acquaintance and of her continued patronage for many years to come.

Yours truly,
V. R. Trochere

Foxhole Farm
Lower Downe
Sodbury
Wiltshire

6 March

Darling Dru,

I was pleased to see you in such sparkling form last night. Is that your new young man? I do wish you didn't have to wear such low-cut dresses.

What did you think of your future stepmother? Frankly, I thought she was ghastly, although obviously I'd never dream of saying so to your father.

As promised, I'm not ringing you in the office, but please let me know before you fly off. I am seriously worried about Claire. She sounds so *very* different in her letters.

Must dash, lots of love,
Mummy

2 Abraham's Close
Finchley Road
London NW8

6 March

Dearest Anthony,

Thank you for inviting David and me to your little gathering to meet Yasmin. What an exotic creature she is, so different from both Caroline and your American wife.

It was lovely to see Drucilla getting on so well with her new boyfriend. He seemed a nice chap, though rather hearty, if you know what I mean, and he obviously couldn't take his eyes off her plunging neckline.

David is trying really hard to plug your book. He finds it so disheartening when he fails to sell his favourite authors. Takes it personally, you know. Unfortunately it's not, if you don't mind me saying so, what one could call a very popular subject.

When we got home last night, he mentioned to me that perhaps you should take advantage of Yasmin's background and write something about Persia. *Treasures of the Shah* or something. David feels that this could have some real mileage.

I was delighted to see your mother in her usual form, although she did seem a little worried about poor Arthur.

Joseph is so pleased you are coming to his Bar Mitzvah next weekend. You are his favourite godparent, you know!

Look forward to seeing you then and thank you again for dinner. That caviar was a real treat.

With love from us both,
Annabel

The Old Rectory
Wet Waltham
Near Rottingdean
Sussex

6 March

Tony darling,

Thank you for including me in the group to meet your
new wife to be – I'm only sorry I didn't have any chance
to get to know her. I was so busy chatting to Caroline about
the girls, catching up on Ivor's news and talking to your
other friends, as well as having a nice cosy natter with Mrs
Kettle. What a find she was, even if she does go on about
her health.

Claire is obviously worrying Caroline a lot, although I
don't quite see why. If you live among flowers it must be
lovely. Personally I would have thought that Drucilla's life
in the City was much more dubious. All those wild young
stockbrokers and bankers. She was looking pretty, though
I cannot help wishing that the clothes the young wear
these days were a little less risqué.

Uncle Arthur didn't sound much better this morning but
he was so pleased you came to see him – even though the
tip you gave him for Sandown cost him a fortune and very
nearly caused another stroke.

I have arranged to have tea with Madame . . . I've
forgotten her name, next week, so perhaps I'll get to know
her better then. Has she been somewhere in the sun lately?
So bad for the skin.

All my love, darling,
Mummy

43

Winchester Park
Under Wallop
Hampshire

8 March

My darling Ant-Pant,

Charles and I were so touché and too thrilled for words
to be at your intimate little dinner party to meet your
enchanting new bride-to-be. I have completely taken her
under my wing and am going to introduce her to my
hairdresser, my manicurist, my couturier, my jeweller and
also show her a few of my favourite little haunts.

When you get back from Paris you simply must come and
spend a weekend here at the Park. Easter would be perfect
for us, as we always like to fill the house with guests and
invite our most amusing locals over for various meals, and
of course there's the point-to-point on Easter Monday here.

I feel that we could really launch darling Jasmin in style.
The daffodils should be out by then and the garden looking
lovely.

I hadn't seen Drucilla since she was little. What a big girl
she's grown into. Luckily I never had to worry about
Fenella's weight. She's so like me with her petite figure,
tiny feet and blond curls.

Must dash for an appointment with my masseuse.

Thanks again for a simply gorgeous evening, sweetie.

Masses of love,
Fi-fi

44

181a Battersea Bridge Road
Lower Chelsea
London SW11

10 March

Darling Mummy,

I had a feeling you didn't take to Daddy's new bit but I
doubt if it will last long, so don't worry. She obviously
hated me for some reason.

Of course I'll let you know before I leave for the Far East
but don't worry about Claire. She's much better at looking
after herself than I am, if you only knew it.

I thought Daddy was in cracking form but I wasn't too
sure about his new purple and pink quilted smoking-jacket.
He needs a haircut too. He's trying to dissuade me from
going away. Do you know why?

See you next weekend.

Lots of love,
Dru

PS: Thanks for saying I can bring Rupert. He's mad on
riding so he'll help exercise the horses. I'm paying my phone
bill this week, so with any luck they'll re-connect it soon.

181a Battersea Bridge Road
Lower Chelsea
London SW11

10 March

Darling Daddy,

Thanks for letting me join the group to meet your Persian.
I don't think she liked me much. She's very beautiful, but
she seemed to think I was a rival bird rather than your
daughter. She kept asking me how long I'd known you. I
wish my French was better. Please try and look your age
sometimes (and behave it). I think Mummy was slightly
embarrassed. 'All that purring and pawing in public is so
common' is what she said to me in the loo after dinner.
Typical Mummy!
    What did you think of Rupert? He's a bit of a 'jolly good
show' sort, isn't he, but you should see him in his uniform.
I'm hoping he might invite me to the Sandhurst Ball.
    I suggested lunch with Hyacinth or whatever her name is
but she didn't sound frightfully keen. Perhaps *you* could
explain who I am. I'll think about cancelling my trip to the
Far East but I've paid for the flight now and put a huge
deposit down on the truck so it might be a bit late.

Lots of love,
D

she seemed to think I was a rival bird

Hock Hall
Hove

10 March

My dear Tony,

What I'd like to know is how do you do it? That stunner
is the same age as Drucilla, or certainly looks it. It was
decent of you to ask me to dine. Really pushing the boat
out . . . caviar. You'd better watch out the young lady
doesn't think she is marrying a millionaire as well as a
lady-killer!

I had a word with David and he sounded a trifle pessimistic
about your latest book. I can't think why you never take
my advice and continue with thrillers. Why not set a
whodunnit at Hock Hall? Call it 'What's your poison?' and
I'll give you some tips about dirty work in the fermentation
vat. By the way, I liked Drucilla's young man. Had a chat
to him over the port about the merits of Cirencester versus
Sandhurst.

It was nice to see the Hampshires. Charles is such a good
man. I like his dry sense of humour, although Fiona can
be dreadfully tiresome. Cotton wool between the ears, poor
dear. Mother seemed even more gaga than ever. Senile
dementia setting in fast, I'd wager. She hardly recognized
me, kept calling me Ivor!

Well, many thanks again, old cock. See you on Wednesday
at the Parson's Rest!

Yours ever,
Geoffrey

PS: I ran into that rather loud friend of Witney's playing
golf yesterday. It seems your American ex is not taking
the news as well as Caroline.

The Officers' Mess
Sandhurst College
Camberley
Surrey

12 March

Dear Sir Anthony,

I'm sorry this letter is tardy but we have just come back from a week on manoeuvres.

It was very kind of you to ask Dru to invite me to such a super dinner last week to meet your fiancée. It was a super evening and I enjoyed myself. I'm afraid I rather over-indulged on your excellent port but luckily I didn't get stopped by the fuzz.

We are being posted to Germany shortly but I very much hope to see Dru before I leave. She's such a super girl.

I also much enjoyed my conversation with your brother, sir. He told me to think about what I could do when I left the army. He was awfully keen on the unusual satisfactions of wine growing, especially it seems in Chile. Frightfully interesting, but if I ever reach that part of the world I'm much more likely to end up in the Falklands, or somewhere equally ghastly.

Thank you again for such a super time, sir.

Yours sincerely,
Rupert Tiddlesworth

The Officers' Mess
Sandhurst College
Camberley
Surrey

12 March

Dear Dru,

I have just written your father a rather belated letter to thank him for dinner. It was a super evening and you were looking stunning.

Any chance of you coming to the Sandhurst Ball? It should be quite a giggle. Do say yes.

Love from
Rupert

PS: If you can come, please wear that dress again. It was great news.

Winchester Park
Under Wallop
Hampshire

12 March

My dear Drucilla,

It was so lovely to see you again the other night after all
these years, and looking so blooming. How time flies!
What a darling your new mother seems. I'm sure you two
will be the greatest of friends. And your father looks so radiant
and in love. Such an attractive man. I'm afraid we fell out
a while ago, as he took a great fancy to me, but that's all
another story and water under the bridge by now.

The point of this letter, dear, is to say that I have invited
Jasmin and your father to stay for Easter with a few of our
nearest and dearest, and as Fenella is having some of her
little friends I wondered if you would like to come too?

Let me know as soon as possible, dear, as the staff like to
get the numbers straight in plenty of time.

Yours affectionately,
With love,
Fiona (Hampshire)

Poste Restante
PO Box IM12
Bali
Indonesia

1 March

Dearest brothers,

I am writing to you about my life here and to tell you how grateful I am to your mother for recommending me this wonderful place. It has changed my whole outlook on living, thinking, eating, music and activities in general. Peace, beauty and nature is basically our motto – a far cry from life in big cities today. I was disillusioned, as you know, with the gurus and Moonies. I am very happy and I hope you are both happy too.

I hear that our father is to marry again. No one I have heard from seems very happy about this but I feel sure there is no need for doubt as she is called Jasmin. Here we all believe that flowers make for happiness, and with her name she will surely make Father and everyone else happy.

Do not worry about things like work, dearest brothers. Work is unnecessary in life and never makes people either happy or at peace.

Blessings and love from
Your 'flower' sister,
Claire

Winchester Park
Upper Wallop
Hampshire

12 March

Geoff darling,

It was so wonderful to see you at Ant-Pant's dinner party
after all these years. You have been so frightfully busy –
with all your planting and pruning and picking.

Might there be a teensy-weensy chance of tête-à-tête
drinkie in London with you some time soon? I'm so
dreadfully worried about Ant-Pant wanting to actually marry
this Arabian girl, and feel it is all on the rebound from a
little indiscretion he and I had a few years ago. (Not a word
to Charles!)

Of course I have made bosom friends with Jasmin, and
I'm sure I'll be able to make her presentable to our friends,
but it won't be easy, even for little old me.

Please ring soon. The mornings are best, as Charles is
always out and about, but not before 11.30 a.m., darling!
I need my beauty sleep.

A bientôt,
Masses of love,
Fi

53

Box 2242
Running Dog Rapids
Juneau
Alaska

4 March

Dear Arthur,

Thank you for your letter about Teddy's demise. It was
kind of you to write, especially as I know you never
approved of my marriage to him. In fact, the only one who
supported me at the time was Ivor, the black sheep of the
family now, I hear.

I gather from Primmy that you are doing well on the
racecourse and at the backgammon tables, but also knocking
back the old booze a bit. We must watch it at our age, dear
brother. What happened to your idea of becoming a
trainer? Too much effort, I suppose. Exercising the dogs
here keeps me fit, especially in this bracing air.

Come and pay me a visit some time. Haven't seen you
since we came over for Anthony's wedding twenty-five years
ago.

Love,
Violet

Winchester Park
Under Wallop
Hampshire

13 March

Drucilla dear,

Did you get my invitation for the Easter weekend? We are so hoping you are coming. Fenella is dying to see you again, and I'm sure you two will have lots in common.

I'm so sorry to hear from a French friend of mine that you did not go to your father's wedding in Paris. He must have been disappointed that none of the family were there. But c'est la vie, I suppose.

Look forward to hearing from you, soon, please dear.

Affectionately,
Fiona Hampshire

The Fortress

15 March

Dear Pop,

Mom wrote us a card from Lyford Cay and said she
wanted us back in the States for the Easter vacation but
you promised we could go skiing. What gives?

Druci came and took us out to tea today with a soldier
boy. She said you were in Paris getting married and that
our stepmother is a smasher. Druci had an awful hangover
as she'd been to some bash the night before. We had a
letter from Claire last week telling us about her life in Bali
and it sounds real weird. Is she coming home soon?

You might get a note from Mr Teak (our housemaster)
but pay no attention. We've dealt with the problem between
us and it was totally over-exaggerated anyway.

Try and pacify Mom. She's real mad at you, even tho'
she pushed off with that TV guy in the first place. I
suppose it's because he ditched her – maybe that's why she
wants us in the vacation. Gee it makes you feel like any
old piece of junk furniture.

Please write and let us know about the skiing.

Love from us both,
C and W

The Intercontinental Hotel
Teheran
Iran

28 March

My one and only love,

I ring and ring but no one answer. Where are you? I am so sorry I leave you just three weeks after our marriage but must sort out problems with children. Reza he is being so difficult – he is fighting mouth and finger – how you say? But soon I will be back in your arms . . . Thank you for the beautiful times in Paris. I am so much missing the touch of your tender hands on my body, the sweetness of your lips on mine, even the garlic. You are such a wonderful lover.

Poor old Mama is not well. She has never been the same since the Shah he left. I try and try to tell her to return to Papa in Paris but she is terrible obstinate.

The children are so happy to see me and Fatima would like to come to London, but Parviz he prefer to stay with his father, and Reza say it is a sin to split them. I am very confused.

The bite on my leg has infection so I have seen a doctor. I do not understand why that nasty Fred no like me. Please please send him to your horse wife. She talk about animals all the time. I hope that bossy old woman she look after you?

Sorry, mon amour, but I might have to come back here next month if Reza insist on going to the court. Fernando is again here for the business. He very kind.

I am dying to be with you. We will make beautiful baby with blond hair and blue eyes. I always wanted.

I bring you lots more Persian caviar, and of course I go to countryside with your Lord and Lady friends. I buy English country clothes when I come.

All my love,
Yasmin

57

Sir Anthony,

I am leaving this note, begging your pardon, but I'm afraid I am giving in my notice. I'm ever so sorry to have to do this to such a gentleman and after all these years but I don't know that I've ever been spoken to like that in all my born days. As you know, sir, my place here is in the kitchen but I've always been happy to give Phyllis a hand with a bit of dusting, ironing, or whatever seems fit, but I'm afraid I was never trained to be a lady's maid and, if you pardon the cheek, sir, your lady-wife is no lady. Now your lovely mother, God bless her, and the Lady Caroline, them's what I call ladies. Miss Drucilla and Miss Claire, well I've known them since they was born. Even the American lady had time to chat with me sometimes, and although her language was direct she was never rude to me, and them naughty twins, forever having me on, are good boys really.

But I've come to the end of my tether now, sir, so I'll be packing up and going to stay with my daughter in Watford. I'll be glad of the company of my grandchildren during the day.

God bless you, sir.

Yours respectfully,
M. A. Kettle

your lady-wife's no lady

Sloane's
Slough

28 March

Dear Sir Anthony,

Further to our discussions on the progress and conduct of your sons, I very much regret having to inform you that one of them was caught last week by the History tutor in a serious indiscretion, on which it would be improper to enlarge in a letter. The maid concerned has naturally been asked to leave, but the grave problem still remains as to which of your twins is the culprit. Both have denied any knowledge of the incident. One was seen playing rugger at the time in question and the other was briefly spotted in the Lab, the Art Room and the Library all at the same time by various other boys, which in itself is quite an achievement.

We considered rusticating them both but have decided to overlook the matter as it almost coincides with the end of the term. No doubt you will want to have a serious talk with them during the holidays.

The boys' work has shown a marked improvement this term, although it is curious that their essays in English and History, and their Maths and Biology reports, seem to vary so much from week to week. For example, at the beginning of term Charles's English showed great promise, while Warren's was rather poor. Lately it is the reverse. The same applies to Latin and French, only vice versa. Their mother came to see me briefly after half-term but I'm afraid that she has a somewhat curious and lighthearted approach to progress and discipline.

May I take this opportunity to congratulate you on your recent marriage.

Yours sincerely,
Tom Teak

quite an achievement

24 Louisburg Square
Beacon Hill
Boston
Mass.

25 March

Tone,

The boys claim that they like that rotten school now. I
don't believe it. How can you like such an unwelcoming,
cold and dreary place, humorless teachers and such fucking
awful plumbing? And all that old-fashioned pomposity. I
just had to laugh.

I gave the boys a fun weekend. We stayed at the
Connaught and went to the movies, the theater, McDonald's,
etc., (You'll be getting the check.)

Charlie says you are taking them skiing over Easter but
as that bitch Drucilla told me you were going to stay with
those snobby Hampshires I want them here with me. After
all, you had them for Christmas, so it's my turn.
Goddammit, they are half American.

Send them each an open round-trip ticket to Boston and
I'll book them back.

Witney

PS: What I'd like to know is what was the history guy doing
in the maid's room anyway? Hoping to get lucky too, I
guess.

Poste Restante
PO Box IM12
Bali
Indonesia

19 March

Dearest Father,

I have some wonderful news. I am with child. I do not know if the father is Poppy, Dogrose, Xaviour or Bull-Finch, but they are happy for me and all hope it is theirs. I am also writing to Mother but I'm afraid she will not understand.

I have a favour to ask. Due to certain medical problems over the past five months, I have been advised to have the baby in England. Please may I come and stay with you in London and give birth at home? (I do not believe in hospitals or unnatural childbirth.) I will only bring two or three of the crowd with me.

I hope you are happy with your new 'flower'. I look forward to meeting her. I am praying that she might also be filled with your seed. My little bud would then have a friend.

I look forward to hearing your answer.

Blessings from your loving daughter,
Claire

Veld & Leikt
1 Bedford Street
London W1

2 April

Dear Lady Hampshire,

How kind of you to ask me to stay for Easter but I'm afraid I am unable to accept your invitation, as I am hoping to go abroad.

It was indeed nice to see you again after such a long time. Simply ages!

The reason that none of the family went to Daddy's registry office wedding in Paris was that we had all agreed not to. He was not disappointed, on the contrary he was relieved.

Yours sincerely,
Drucilla

Foxhole Farm
Lower Downe
Sodbury
Wiltshire

3 April

Dear Tony,

What are we to do about Claire? I wish you'd listened to me when I told you I was worried.

I gather she's written to you asking to stay, bringing her whole entouràge and producing her half-caste illegitimate in London. I'll get on to Mr Born and see if he can arrange an abortion but if it's too late by then we'll just have to think of something else. At least she sounds over the moon. Quite extraordinary!

Please have your telephone mended. It's very boring and time-consuming always to have to write long letters. You know I never did one of those secretarial courses and I'm very busy at the moment with the hunter trials.

I have talked to Drucilla about Claire. She's rather upset, and a little bitter. They used to get on so well, but I think Dru feels, and perhaps rightly, that we have paid more attention to Claire lately.

I'm coming to London next week. Could we meet to discuss the problem, preferably in a restaurant as I don't really want to come to the house, particularly now that Mrs Kettle has left.

I will have Fred for you if you really want but won't you miss him? Also one of my bitches is in season at the moment so it's not the best time.

Love,
Caroline

Hock Hall
Hove

3 April

My dear Mama,

I'm not sure how much it is my business, but I am very concerned about Uncle Arthur. I was in the Harley Street area this afternoon, dentist you know, and thought I'd look in on the old boy for a cup of tea. He was sitting up in bed gulping down a tumbler of vintage port, the *Sporting Life* on his lap, TV on full-blast, and talking on the telephone to his bookmaker. I know he is in the best of hands but frankly he was rather flushed, perspiring freely and his breathing was laboured. I hope I did not overstay my welcome.

I don't want to worry you unduly, Mama, but I thought a word from you to Matron would not go amiss.

Your loving son,
Geoffrey

PS: Apparently British Telecom have push-button telephones but with the same old ringing tone. Would you like me to order them for you?

frankly he was rather flushed

The Old Rectory
Wet Waltham
Near Rottingdean
Sussex

7 April

Darling,

Thank you for your sweet letter about poor Uncle Arthur.
Yes, it is sad and rather sudden, and since your father
died I had leaned on him a lot. But he went very peacefully,
and after that last mammoth stroke he would have lived a
miserable existence, so it's probably for the best.

It is so thoughtful of you to suggest giving a luncheon
after the cremation on Wednesday. I'm sure his friends
and yours would appreciate that, particularly those of them
who live in the country. Not many relations around, I'm
afraid, what with Violet and Ivor such continents away, but
hopefully Geoffrey will postpone his trip to South
America.

Will someone be able to do for you now that dear Mrs
Kettle has left?

Thank you, darling.

Your loving mother

30f Welbeck Street
London W1

7 April

My dear Anthony,

I have studied your recent medical report from RECUPA
and, while you have a clean bill of health and appear very fit
for your age, there is one minor problem which I would like
to test regarding that little trouble you had a few years
ago. In view of your recent marriage I feel it would be
prudent to check up on this matter.
Give my secretary a ring and make an appointment at
your earliest convenience.

All the best,
Yours,
Christopher Henderson

Winchester Park
Under Wallop
Hampshire

7 April

My darling Ant-Pant,

I'm so dreadfully sorry about the hideous disasters over
the weekend. What with the heating breaking down, the
perfectly appalling weather and that naughty horse kicking
Jasmin, I'm not surprised you left on Sunday morning.
Such a shame, as the rest of the weekend was lovely. The
sun shone, the point-to-point was gorgeous as usual, and
it was even warm enough to have a little game of croquet on
Monday. I had absolutely no idea that the Ashtraizs were
such intimate friends of Jasmin's ex-husband; so
embarrassing. They are our new neighbours, you see, and I
thought that it would have made her more at home amongst
all the English crowd. Obviously I was mistaken. Silly
little me, I do apologize, darling. The scene at dinner on
Saturday evening was simply mortifying, but Jasmin was
absolutely magnificent. She looked so beautiful when she
stood up and threw the candelabra.

I hope by now all is forgiven and that we will still be
friends. Let me know when she gets back from Teheran
and I'll do my usual tactful best to patch things up. Let's
hope you will have paid the phone people by then. What
an exorbitant amount, but Jasmin talking to her children
for two hours every afternoon would mount up, I suppose.

I'm so desperately sorry that Jasmin's first visit to the
Park was so catastrophic. I hope next time will be better,
presuming you will be able to persuade her to give us another
chance.

Lots of love from us both, and again many apologies,
Fiona

that naughty horse

Veld & Leikt
1 Bedford Street
London W1

8 April

Darling Daddy,

Yet another badly typed letter to say how sorry I am about
Great Uncle Arthur. I gather the dreaded Yasmin's away
again (sorry, but I'm afraid I don't like her), so can I come
to supper one evening? I'll cook. I want to talk to you
about several problems: boyfriends, money, etc., but mainly
about Claire. Is it true that she's about to arrive pregnant
and covered in flowers (pot-plants more likely!) and staying
at home? I've talked to Mummy but she doesn't make
much sense – either she's in a panic about it or rushing off
to the stables, so it's hopeless.

I suppose I'll have to cancel my trip now. I wonder if
they'll ever refund all that money?

That wretched Italian woman you fancied last year keeps
ringing me in the office, which pisses my boss off
something rotten. Can't you tell her the form or something?

I'll drop by on Monday or Tuesday evening unless I get
word to the contrary.

Love,
Dru

PS: Would you like me to come and do lunch after the
funeral?

The Intercontinental Hotel
Teheran
Iran

8 April

My one and only,

Comme d'habitude missing you but Reza is in better temper this time. Maybe he find new girlfriend.

I have good flight here as I sit next to Fernando, who again come on the business. He help me carry my things and take me to hotel, where he also stay. He invite me to dinner tonight. Maybe I say yes as I lonely in the night without you. It would be company and change, no? The children they seem all right, but Parviz he no talk much. I so longing for you to meet them. I try to fix with Reza that they stay in the summer with us. Perhaps we take boat in South of France for a time and have vacances en famille. Fernando he is in shipping business so I will poke his brain.

Je suis désolée à cause de ce weekend, but jamais I go again to that freezing house, with those horrible people.

I will cable you when I come.

Your
Yasmin

PS: Fernando say he know you but would prefer to no talk about it. Why?

73

Winchester Park
Under Wallop
Hampshire

11 April

Annabel dear,

I'm so dreadfully worried about Ant-Pant and wondered if you knew what's going on or if there was anything I could do. With David's book connections you see so much more of him than we do. Although the last thing I want to do is interfere, I just want to help.

He seem so distrait these days. Perhaps it is because Jasmin is already almost permanently away, poor darling, trying to sort out her life. And of course the old lady must be an added burden, mourning for that alcoholic brother of hers. I don't imagine that lump of a daughter is much comfort either, or the other girl, drugged to the eyeballs and now pregnant, I gather. I would *so* like to be of assistance as my Charlie is such an old friend of Ant-Pant, but I feel so helpless and fragile.

You probably heard about the disastrous weekend. What did they say to you about it? It really wasn't *my* fault.

Aren't your Joseph and Ant-Pant's twins the same age? He told me about Joseph's Confirmation service. It sounded too quaint for words.

As you know, I'm basically a lady of leisure, apart from running the Park and all my various charities, etc. Such a nightmare having a title. *Absolutely* everybody wants one to be chairman of *absolutely* everything.

I am relying on you, dear, to keep me in touch. As you know, I won't tell a soul.

With love,
Fiona

2 April

Most Honourable British Lord,

I have had no communication from you regarding your daughter, and my proposal of marriage. Did I not meet with your requirements, your expectations?

I am instructing my aides to draw up a detailed list of all my assets and wealth. Perhaps then you will consider me worthy of your treasured offspring.

I cannot rest until I hear from you. I dream of her voluptuous soft breasts, to squeeze them again and feel those hard little pink nipples. Her milky white flesh was so erotic to touch; like the silk lining of my tents in the desert.

I am planning to return to your illustrious city in the last week of May. Perhaps I could call on you in person. May I suggest the last Thursday of the month, at your evening drinking hour?

Most truly, I am,
Ahbed Soluvly

2 Abraham's Close
Finchley Road
London NW8

11 April

My dear Anthony,

I'm sorry we couldn't come to lunch after that nice service
for your poor uncle last week, but we were in a terrible
hurry to get to Sotheby's. They were auctioning a lovely old
desk which David was very keen on. Unfortunately it was
way beyond our price range. Apparently a rich Persian
woman had left an exorbitant bid on it. Poor David is
rather disappointed. I know you authors like to work at
shabby old tables, but David's not like that.

I have written your dear mother a note of condolence.
She will miss her brother, won't she.

Will we be seeing you at Foyle's literary lunch next week?
Perhaps not this year.

Fondest love from us both,
Annabel

Hock Hall
Hove

11 April

My dear Tony,

Poor old Uncle Arthur, but what a good way to go! He
may not have known it but apparently he died as the
winner of the Grand National came in. Just the way he
would have wanted it!

Thank you for lunch after the funeral. I was relieved to
see Mama holding up all right, but I hope one of you will
see to it that I join the worms in Mother Earth. Those
crematoriums are so impersonal.

Hope all goes well with the new wife. Why wasn't she
there? See you on Monday, and don't forget what I told
you about the Santiago fish. In or out of water, they are all
ready to tease, tickle or fry! I'm glad you're at least showing
some interest.

All the best and thanks again,
Geoffrey

The Beach
Cobblers Cove
Barbados

1 April

Tony, Tony, How do you do, you townie, you?

Trouble and strife in your city life with your new wife?
Perhaps you don't give a damn with your girl from
Teheran. But here on the beach, life is a peach. Don't buy
it, try it. Here in the sun I offer you fun, my son, my
nephew, no curfew.

Come write with me, let's write and write away – There's
reams of paper and gallons of ink in the brilliant moonlit
bay. I say no more – but please dear boy . . . think anew –

adieu . . .
Ivor

here on the beach, life is a peach

2 Abraham's Close
Finchley Road
London NW8

11 April

Dear Fiona,

As you say, Anthony has a lot on his plate at the moment but I think it's much better not to interfere. He has always been rather a closed book, and at present this is truer than it sounds. Frankly, I don't think he'd take kindly to your so-called help. David is busy encouraging his writing: his mother has never been a burden; more a prop! Contrary to what you imagine, Drucilla is a great comfort to her father, although naturally he is worried about Claire at the moment.

Joseph is indeed a great friend of Charles and Warren, and although they attend different schools their half-terms coincide and Anthony has kindly asked us to supper on the last Thursday in May as they have all been invited to a teenage disco-party later that evening.

Regards to Charles and love to you both,
Annabel

30f Welbeck Street
London W1

18 April

My dear Anthony,

Nice to see you the other day, although I'm sorry to hear about the financial side of life. Why don't you write a book on humour? Even as a therapy or something? With your wide knowledge of humanity and a varied group of international friends, coupled with your attitude to life, it could win the Nobel Prize!

As the RECUPA tests showed, you are clearly very fit. Stable weight, regular heartbeat, blood pressure, and so on. I did very much regret having to give you the results of the other tests, which showed the 99 per cent sterility problem. This is, as I predicted, due to that little mishap a few years back. I hope you are by now a little more reconciled: these things are always depressing, even to a father of four!

Naturally this is confidential and it's entirely up to you whether you wish to tell your new wife – whom I still have not had the pleasure of meeting.

Drucilla comes for a check-up from time to time. What a nice girl she is. Good luck, old boy.

Yours,
Christopher

Poste Restante
PO Box IM12
Bali
Indonesia

10 April

Dear Father,

I am planning to arrive in the English spring time. We have found a boat which takes a long time but is cheap.

Thank you for your cable agreeing that we can stay. Don't worry about the space as we are all used to sharing the floor. We also bring our own candles, soap, sponges, and a toothbrush. We only wash once a week as it is so much healthier. Mother did not sound very happy with the situation, which is a pity as everyone in life should always be happy. She also suggested killing the baby. What an awful idea. Please talk to her.

I wonder if my sister will stand by me during my coming uplifting experience. I look forward to being reacquainted with her, although I do not think we will have much in common any more.

I hope you will not be confused that my friends here call me Lily. It is my new name.

Your loving daughter,
Claire

Foxhole Farm
Lower Downe
Sodbury
Wiltshire

15 April

Dear Tony,

I dropped by the house this afternoon on my way home but no one was there. For God's sake get the telephone back on. It's a nightmare.

Mr Born says it's too late for an abortion, but hopefully he will come to the house for the actual birth as I really can't see all those 'hippies' coping.

Are you really going to have them all to stay? Claire wrote that they would be all right but I seem to remember her room being quite small, and Drucilla's old bedroom will have to be kept aside for the baby and the monthly nurse.

Your mother has written to ask if she can stay with us for a weekend at the end of May. Something about dry rot at the Rectory.

Drucilla seems a bit in the dumps at having to put off her holiday. She tells me she cooked the lunch after poor old Arthur's funeral. (Sorry I couldn't make it.)

Cecil's going into the local Nuffield for a prostate operation some time soon. I gather it's rather painful, but luckily he doesn't know because he can't hear a word the doctor says!

Love,
Caroline

Hoare's Bank
33 Fleet Street
London EC4

20 April

Dear Sir Anthony,

I observe that the payments which have recently been debited to your account have occasioned an overdraft of £295,000 according to our records at the close of business yesterday.

In the circumstances, I thought I should bring it to your attention and I would be glad if you will kindly arrange for sufficient funds to be remitted to cover the overdraft.

Perhaps it is not my concern but I feel it would have been more prudent to have opened a separate account for your wife. As you will see from the enclosed cheques, most of them bear her signature.

I am pleased to inform you that Drucilla's account is in the clear at present and a recent cheque from a travel agent has put her in credit for the first time ever!

I look forward to hearing from you and hope we will be able to come to a satisfactory arrangement.

Yours truly,
Harry Till

2 Abraham's Close
Finchley Road
London NW8

22 April

My dear Anthony,

It was so kind of you to attend Joseph's Bar Mitzvah. It must have been double Dutch to you, but he was very touched that you came.

What a good idea for us all to get together at the start of half-term on Thursday, 29 May. I gather from Annabel that you have kindly invited us to an early supper before the boys go off to some party.

It is a shame about your book, but I'm afraid that I still can't get any publisher interested. We must get together very soon to discuss the future. By the way, your telephone is out of order. I have reported it, so I hope it will be fixed soon. What an inconvenience it must be.

Yours,
David

Sloane's
Slough

24 April

Dear Pop,

Thanks for meeting us at the airport. Mr Teak was furious
we were a week late. We tried to explain it wasn't our fault
but if you could write too it might help. We had a big
problem getting Mom to book us a flight back. We tried
calling you but your line was dead.

Life was pretty dreary in the vac. Mom has a new date,
a guy who runs an antique shop in the city, so she was
mostly out and we just got on with it, and getting on with
it in Boston is getting on with FA.

Druci came down last Sunday. She seemed a bit low what
with cancelling her holiday and her boyfriend going off to
Germany. She said she was thinking of going to Cairo instead
but we tried to talk her out of it.

We feel pretty grown-up now that we are going to be
uncles. Is Claire going to marry the weirdo father? Could we
bring a couple of friends to stay for half-term? They live in
Nigeria so have no place to go. It's from Thursday, 29
May, through Wednesday, 4 June.

We'll try calling you again as soon as your phone's back
on the hook.

Love,
Charlie and Warren

Sloane's
Slough

26 April

Dear Sir Anthony,

It was a pity that your sons arrived late for the start of term but I'm glad to report that they have caught up very well. I would like to take this opportunity of saying how grateful I am to them for being so considerate and helpful towards my daughter, who has joined us here in the house to study for her 'O' Levels. While most of the other boys of that age either ignore or tease her, Charles and Warren are most solicitious, spending much of their precious free-time helping her with homework in their room.

I hate to raise the subject, Sir Anthony, but the Bursar informs me that you have not paid the school fees. I would be grateful if you could rectify this matter.

Yours sincerely,
Tom Teak

24 Louisburg Square
Beacon Hill
Boston
Mass.

6 May

Tone,

The boys write that their mid-term break is end May/
beginning June. I was planning to take two weeks in Europe
this summer so maybe I'll do England over that period.
Don't panic. I'm not expecting to stay with you. London
hotels are pretty booked up between April and September,
but we'll find someplace. Whatever happens I'll come and
visit with Charlie and Warren. We'll probably hit London
the Tuesday or Wednesday so will come by Thursday
evening 29 May and take a drink off you.

Witney

PS: I'm getting into the antique business with Georgie, a
    new friend of mine, so England should be a good place to
    look around. Plenty of antiques where you are concerned,
    I seem to remember!

Box 2242
Running Dog Rapids
Juneau
Alaska

23 April

My dear Anthony,

As all your relations of my generation are so wet and
weedy, how about *you* coming to stay with me? As it must be
coming up to your 25th wedding anniversary, if I'm not
mistaken, why not treat all the family to a glacier skiing
holiday. Bring the animals too! The more the merrier! All
the best my dear.

Affectionately,
Your Aunt Violet

PS: Let me know how many of you to expect, and I shall
send you the tickets. Teddy left me a fortune, so I can
afford it! V.

The Boat

3 May

Dearest Father,

Just a note which I will post from Djibouti where we are docking for a few days to tell you that we will be arriving at the end of May. I assure you that we will be no trouble, as I mentioned in my last letter.

You will be pleased to hear that I am in the best of health but I think I am expecting twins as I am very large for my time. Perhaps it runs in the family.

The boat is due in Southampton at midday on Thursday, 29 May, so we should be with you by teatime if we take the bus. But we might hitch-hike.

I am joyous at the prospect of our family reunion.

Your happy daughter,
Lily (Claire)

Dambeme & Co. Ltd
Mendit-on-Tyne
Merseyside

6 May

Dear Sir,

I enclose an invoice for the advance payment required before we are able to commence the treatment to Lady Haslemere's dry rot in her back passage. Whilst it might appear somewhat exorbitant, you will appreciate the need for our best professional skills in what you will understand is a most delicate piece of work.

Thanking you in advance.

Yours truly,
R. U. Crumlin

Foxhole Farm
Lower Downe
Sodbury
Wiltshire

12 May

Dear Mrs Kettle,

I hope you are comfortable and happy with your daughter and son-in-law in Watford. Your grandchildren must be a handful and I'm sure they are grateful for your help.

I do hope your gout is better now the cold spell is over. Did you ever see the doctor about that swelling?

Mrs Kettle, I have a great favour to ask you. Is there any chance of you coming back to my ex-husband just for a week or two at the end of May? The house will be rather full then and a little help would be so appreciated – frankly, in my opinion, necessary. I quite understand if you can't – I am just asking, in fact begging!

Fondest love,
Yours sincerely,
Caroline Barker

21 Pudding Lane
Watford

14 May

M'lady,

Thank you for your nice letter. Just for you, and Sir
Anthony of course, I will be pleased to do this favour. Mind
you, I won't be putting up with any lip from 'her royal
highness' so she'd better mind her p's and q's.

I'm much better in myself, thank you for asking. Just a
touch of arthritis and a bad knee, but I manage.

I hope you are well, m'lady, and not tiring yourself with
all them animals.

I will try and arrive early on 29 May. That's a Thursday,
I believe. Then I can get settled in before the weekend.

Yours respectfully,
M. A. Kettle

The Intercontinental Hotel
Teheran
Iran

15 May

Chéri,

Sorry I come only for one week, but now the court case is happening I have to be here. There is good chance I might get together the custody of Parviz and Fatima. Fernando has been most kind in this worrying times. A coincidence he is again here on the business, no?

The case should finish before end of the month, and so I will be in your arms the last days of May. I bring also the children with me, I hope.

Thank you for your letter. I am well, but feel a little bit sick. Perhaps is the sun or rich Persian food.

I am so glad the desk arrived safely. I thought it was good time your chipped old table was replaced. I get the splinters from the edges when I bend to kiss you. It was rather expensive, I know. I will pay you money when Reza has settled with me after the court finish.

Please fix the telephone soon. It is horrible not hearing your voice.

Your loving
Yasmin

The Old Rectory
West Waltham
Near Rottingdean
Sussex

17 May

Darling,

The dry-rot specialists have finally given me a date when
they can start the 'treatment', as they call it. They make
it sound like an illness. I'll be arriving with you the last
Thursday in May and going down to Caroline on the
Saturday morning, then back with you on Monday for the
following week if that suits. Apparently Cecil's having an
operation at the local Nuffield on the 28th, so I will be able
to house-sit for Caroline when she goes to visit him.

I had a postcard from Claire telling me that she was having
a baby.

I feel very hurt that you didn't tell me that she was
married. I suppose she was married in a registry office before
she went away. What a long honeymoon!

Your loving mother

Winchester Park
Under Wallop
Hampshire

19 May

My darling Ant-Pant,

Charles and I wondered if you and your lovely bride would give us another chance and come and stay for the August Bank Holiday weekend?

It should be beautiful weather by then, and Jasmin would look so decorative by our poolside in a bikini, sipping a G and T. I absolutely promise there will be no horrid horses, I will even put the doggies in kennels if necessary, and I won't invite anyone else over or to stay without checking with you both first.

I heard from Fiona that you are having a cocktail party in town at the beginning of the children's half-term. Sadly we won't be around as we are just off to our villa in Antigua for ten days for a little rest and to get a start on the tan. Poor Charlie burns terribly but luckily I go a divine honey colour.

I do so hope you will be able to persuade Jasmin to come. I haven't seen her for simply ages.

Masses of love, darling,
Fi-fi

181A Battersea Bridge Road
Lower Chelsea
London SW11

23 May

Darling Daddy,

I've got slight problems. I handed in my notice as I was
planning to go and see Claire, but as I've now cancelled
my trip due to the wretched circumstances, I tried to get
my job back. Unfortunately I've already been replaced, so
I'm penniless. Also my flat was broken into last night and
the buggers took almost everything. I'm trying to get
temping jobs for the moment, and I asked Mummy if I
could go and stay with her, but she seems very busy and,
what with old Cecil's op, Granny, dogs and horses, I don't
think it's quite the moment.

Anyway, I wondered if I could beg a bed for a few days
next week? The sofa would be fine. It's just until they
mend the windows. I promise I'll help in the kitchen, be
tidy and try and get on better with Yasmin this time, if
she's back.

I'm going to Germany this weekend, and driving back
through France, so I'll be with you on Wednesday, the 28th,
if that's OK.

Thanks in advance.

Lots of love,
Dru

30f Welbeck Street
London W1.

24 May

My dear Anthony,

Enclosed the prescription for the 200 Drugadons you
require. I hope you have a nice holiday and a successful start
to the new book you are planning to write, besides a good
rest. I thought you were looking a bit tired and under the
weather. May I suggest that you also buy some extra
Vitamins B and C. With these, plus some good nights'
sleep, you should soon be restored to your old self.

Yours,
Christopher

181a Battersea Bridge Road
Lower Chelsea
SW11

25 May

Dear Rupert,

Thanks for your telegram. Of course I understand that
you had to put off my weekend in Germany. I was just
disappointed, that's all. What a bugger being posted to the
Falklands. Poor you. I would love to see you before you
go, if you've got time. I'm going to be staying at my father's
at the end of the month. How about coming for an early
drink on the 29th and then perhaps I could go to the airport
with you to wave goodbye! Ring me when you get back
to London.

Lots of love,
Dru

The Estate Office
12 Eaton Place
London SW1

2 June

Dear Sir Anthony,

It has come to our attention through complaints from various neighbours in the Square that certain curious odours, noises, shouting, screaming, weird music and the like have been emanating from No. 13, our premises of which you are the leaseholder. These emanations occur both day and night, as do the comings and goings of no less than twenty-four people.

I enclose a copy of the agreement signed by you at the time of occupation and would draw your attention to the clause *'at no time are these said premises to be let or sublet'*.

It is also against the rules for anyone other than those residing in the Square itself to own a key to the gardens. Yet we have received complaints concerning the abundant picking of flowers in the said gardens, which is itself strictly prohibited, as well as several more serious complaints of fornication on the grass and people relieving themselves quite unashamedly behind the bushes.

I trust there is some explanation for these intrusions. If I do not hear from you by return, I'm afraid we will have no further choice but to send in our bailiffs to investigate your premises.

Yours sincerely,
Edward West

more serious complaints of fornication

The Intercontinental Hotel
Teheran
Iran

23 May

Chéri,

A little letter which I hope will arrive before me to tell
you good news! I am expecting your blond, blue-eyed
baby. It was not the weather or rich food that make me sick!

Your
Yasmin

PS: I am arriving Thursday, the 29th, at 4.30 p.m. so I
should be with you by 6.00. I bring Parviz and Fatima, and
am longing for a quiet weekend en famille.

21 Pudding Lane
Watford

2 June

M'lady,

I am writing to say how ever so sorry I am that I couldn't stop on any longer than I did to give a hand, but I just couldn't believe my eyes or ears at the goings-on. I thought I had taken leave of my senses, and was afraid I'd have a stroke.

I hardly recognized Miss Claire – she's put on so much weight; and them filthy dirty friends of hers, it was hard to tell if they was girls or boys. It was nice to see those wicked twins, but who were them darkies? I was ever so relieved when you came and took her ladyship away to the country. She was looking right poorly.

I stayed a while talking to Miss Drucilla, but I'm afraid when that Middle Eastern gentleman arrived in all his flowing robes, and stinking to high heaven of that sickly perfume, I had to go. I was having hallucinations as I could have sworn I saw a snake slithering down the front stairs. Silly old Mrs K., but I just wanted to apologize for having abandoned you all.

Whatever could have kept Sir Anthony?

I trust the Major is recovering from his operation.

Yours respectfully,
M. A. Kettle

2 Abraham's Close
Finchley Road
London NW8

2 June

Dear Lady Haslemere,

I do hope you have recovered from your fainting fit and
spent a restful weekend with Caroline. I must admit that
we were very shocked by the chaos going on at No. 13 too.

I wonder what time Anthony eventually appeared? I only
hope it was before Yasmin was due. I'm afraid I never
took to the American wife very much, who also suddenly
turned up, and as for that gay decorator she had with her,
well, I don't know . . .

The reason for this letter is once again to offer you a bed
in London next week, as obviously you can't possibly go
back to Anthony's house.

Perhaps you will be staying on down in the country, but
if not I just wanted you to know that you will always be
welcome here.

With love from us both,
Annabel

the chaos at No. 13

Foxhole Farm
Lower Downe
Sodbury
Wiltshire

3 June

Darling Drucilla,

I felt terribly guilty leaving you holding the baby (almost literally, judging by the size of Claire), but I just had to get Granny away. I didn't like her colour at all, and was terrified she was about to join Uncle Arthur!

I hope you are coping all right, darling? Thank God you are there. If you need any help I can always pop up, leaving Granny here. Where on earth had Daddy got to?

I had a note from Mrs Kettle apologizing for leaving, rabbiting on about Arabs and snakes. Poor old thing!

Granny had a nice letter from Annabel Goldstein offering her alternative accommodation in London. She mentioned that Witney suddenly appeared for a drink too, with some homosexual in tow. What a nightmare it all sounds. And what with the noise those hippies were making as well, I should think the whole house ought to be fumigated and everyone deloused and checked for AIDS. It made the stables here smell like the Chelsea Flower Show.

Please ring me from a callbox or somewhere as soon as you get this. I'm almost beginning to feel sorry for Yasmin. She must have had a fit when she arrived.

Lots of love,
Mummy

London
England

29 Mai

Cher Papa,

I try to writ in the English, mais we no stay in the England. We no like.

Imagine toi! We go to the new house of Mama, and tout le monde était là, but no the new father. Mama she have hysterics. There are peoples from all around, English, Jewish, American, African, Asian, Arab – also very horrible smell of parfum mélangé avec garlic and poisson mauvais. Some sing, some they swear, one old lady she looked morte, dogs they bark, one fat girl throw flowers all around. It was vraiment terrible.

Please, please we come back to Teheran. Fatima she cry and cry.

Je t'embrasse fort,
Parviz

London
England

1 June

Dearest Brothers, Sisters, Lovers, et al.,

We miss you all and think of you a lot, but Lily has brought us to a home from home. We only wish you were here to share it. There seemed to be many kinds of different people all filled with emotions, some shouting, some screaming, tears pouring from their faces with happiness. An old lady started to wail, in time with our music, and another old lady went into a trance she was so ecstatic. Beside the English people there are also our black brothers, a representative of Allah, friends from the Holy Land, followers of the Ayatollah and people from the New World.

The garden near the house is filled with flowers and the grass is soft and green, so we can make love under the pale blue sky.

Lily is well and happy and looks forward to her father's return. He does not seem to be here yet.

Along with us all she sends you many blessings, love and happiness.

From
Dogrose, Frank and Pansy

Foxhole Farm
Lower Downe
Sodbury
Wiltshire

3 June

Dear Mrs Kettle,

I feel so awful having asked you to come back and help
that weekend. I had no idea, when I said there would be
a lot of people, quite how many! Of course I understand
why you left. I'm very glad you did, as it would have been
very bad for your heart judging by the reports I've heard
since.

You will be pleased to hear that my ex mother-in-law is
recovering remarkably, and my husband is doing as well
as can be expected.

Fond love,
Yours,
Caroline Barker

'Home'

2 June

Darling Mummy,

I hope Granny told you that I've rung up three times and you were permanently out, either riding or visiting Cecil in hospital. There was no point in telling Granny anything so I'm rushing to catch the last post so you'll get this in the morning. *Help!* Please come to London. I simply can't cope any more. Daddy has vanished off the face of the earth, Claire walks around in a trance, and those friends of hers have made the whole house stink. I've tried to keep an eye on the boys and their friends but they are out all day and most of the night, not that I blame them. Witney keeps coming round to see them, and of course it's my fault that they are always out; bitch. Some bloody Arab I met once won't leave me in peace and I've had just about enough. Even the new Spanish daily has walked out.

Please come as soon as possible.

Love,
Dru

As from: Isaac's Street
Hampstead

3 June

Darling Anthony,

I had a pleasant weekend with Caroline. She is such a good, kind and stable person. I really think it's a shame you divorced her.

The garden was looking lovely with the cherry blossom falling like snow and all the azaleas and rhododendrons in full bloom. I am now in London staying with those nice Goldsteins as Caroline had to go away suddenly.

Whatever is going on at the house, darling? I arrived as planned at about 3.00 p.m. on Thursday, very pleased to see Mrs Kettle back and Drucilla looking so well. But then thousands of other people of all shapes, sizes and colours arrived, making the most horrible noise and a lot of mess. I'm afraid I don't remember much more after that, but I am very anxious.

Please let me know what is happening.

Your loving mother

The Intercontinental Hotel
Teheran
Iran

4 June

Cher Antoine,

Where are you? Did you no get my letter? I am your wife.
I am pregnant. I come to you with children and what I
find? A bordel. I was angry, sad, sick and humiliated in
front of Parviz and Fatima. Quelle horreur, la maison, les
gens! Jamais dans ma vie have I such a terrible experience.
I have brought the children home to their father. He was
right. They are better with him.

I should have listen my friends. They tell me that all
Englishmen, especially blond and blue-eyed, are no to
trust. Je me demande an explanation for this nightmare.
Until I hear, I stay.

Yasmin

Sloane's
Slough

6 June

Hi Pop!

We had a great half-term but sorry not to see you. Just as well, tho'. It wasn't really your scene. In fact, frankly, it was nobody's scene, so we were out and about most of the time.

Where did you go and where are you now? Mom arrived with her nancy guy and created something rotten, Granny passed out, Claire's gone bananas and looks like she's going to pop any moment, and as for her friends they make us look like City bank clerks! Your new wife was real mad, screaming and shrieking blue murder, but mostly in French so we couldn't understand. We tried to make friends with her kids but the boy looked down his nose at us and the girl was so scared she was crying. Anyway they didn't stay long.

We managed to persuade the Goldsteins to let Joseph stick around and come to the party with us but they were not very keen.

Druci coped amazingly over the weekend and then her Ma came on Tuesday to help out.

Thanks for letting us have our friends to stay. They had a ball and luckily seemed to think the chaos was pretty normal.

We got back here Wednesday evening on the train.

Please let us know what we are doing in the summer vacation. Mom left for Italy but didn't tell us anything.

Love,
Charlie and Warren

113

The Connaught Hotel
Mount Street
W1

6 June

Tone,

I always had a sneaking feeling you were out of your fucking mind. What the bloody hell are you playing at now? All those shitty people crowded into that crummy house, and no sign of you all weekend. I came by several times to see the boys but they were always out and that dumb daughter of yours didn't know where. I want them back in the States *all* summer.

You are an asshole.

Witney

69 Laxford House
Cundy Street
London SW1

6 June

Antonio,

Che passa? I am going completely mad.

As you never wrote or rang me, even when Fernando was away, I go to see you last Thursday evening.

Not to worry! I was *verry verry* discretto. I sat in the Ferrari, wearing big scarf and the black glasses, just looking at front door. I sit and sit, waiting for what seem like eternity, but you never come.

Tanti other people arrive and leave, some molto strano, but not you . . . never you . . . and then guess what? . . . Who come? Quella stronza and Fernando. Imagino? I could hardly believe my eyes. They come together in grande limosine and, after a big big kiss, she go inside and he drive away.

What is happening, caro!

Eliza

As from: The Goldsteins
London

8 June

Caroline dear,

It was so kind of you to have me to stay for the weekend.
You made me feel so welcome and at home. I much
appreciated it. I enjoyed pottering round the garden with
the dogs but I'm afraid I interfered and did a little weeding
here and there.

Poor Cecil didn't look very comfortable when I saw him
briefly. I do hope he is feeling better now. I meant to ask
you, dear, what exactly is a prostrate operation, apart from
obviously making you prostrate?

I had a nice week in London with the Goldsteins. They
took me to a concert one evening and an exhibition of Israeli
art at the V. and A. on Wednesday afternoon.

I am going down to Rosemary's next weekend so I'll give
you a ring from there to find out how Cecil is. I do wish
Anthony would contact me. Does anyone have any idea
where he is?

Thank you again, dear.

With best love,
Primrose

The Old Rectory
Wet Waltham
Near Rottingdean
Sussex

8 June

My dear Annabel,

Thank you very much for putting me up in your charming
house last week. It was so kind and thoughtful of you and
I thoroughly enjoyed both the concert and the exhibition.
It was sweet of you to include me and I was pleased to
meet Jacob and Ruth. What an interesting couple.

I am glad David is trying to persuade Anthony to go back
to his original style of writing. It was much more successful
and, frankly, easier for me to read. Did he by any chance
mention to David where he was going? He seems to have
disappeared and I'm a little worried about it is as absolutely
nobody seems to know where he has gone.

The dry-rot people have made the most awful mess here
and I won't be able to move back in until after the weekend.
I must go and water the poor flowers now. This dry spell
might be lovely for us but not for my border!

Please let me know if David has word of Anthony.

Thank you once again, dear, for your kind hospitality.

With love,
Primrose Haslemere

Foxhole Farm
Lower Downe
Sodbury
Wiltshire

12 June

Darling Dru,

Thank God I dropped by when I did, even if it was only to see if I could find Granny's glasses. It must have been telepathy, as I should have realized that they would have been in her bag all the time.

How you were coping I'll never know, but I really take my hat off to you, darling.

I always had a difficult time giving birth, which is probably why I never had any more children, but Claire was really going through agonies, poor child, and for so long. I thought Mr Born would never appear. Thank goodness she is now safely in hospital and that funny little slit-eyed baby ensconced here with Mrs Higgins's competent niece. What a bit of luck to find a trained nurse on one's doorstep.

As soon as you have disposed of those ghastly friends of Claire's, I suggest you come down here and have a rest.

By the way, I hope you were not too put off by the birth. It does not mean you will have a problem, darling, I promise.

By all means open Daddy's mail but we can't send it on as we don't know where. I must say he is behaving even more irresponsibly than usual. Rather in character, I'm afraid. I enclose a cheque to pay the telephone bill and have done my utmost to stop the bailiffs from marching in.

Lots of love, and chin up,
Mummy

Hotel Cipriani
Venice
Italy

10 June

You Creep,

Where the fucking hell are you hiding? You're a real shirk jerk! I've written to Mr Fucking Teak and told him to release Charlie and Warren from that stinking hole and send them back on the next plane.

Georgie and I have bought an old palazzo in Venice and are going to do it up. Meanwhile we are roughing it at the Cheapriani! (I'll be sending you the tab!)

By the way, I saw your old Italian bit of pizza sitting alone in a cafe in St Mark's Square. She made a bee-line for me, screaming something about her husband and your new wife. Christ, what a mess you manage to make of your life. Serves you right!

Witney

The Old Rectory
Wet Waltham
Near Rottingdean
Sussex

12 June

Anthony darling,

It is lovely to be back in my own house after being away
for what seems ages. I had a very pleasant weekend with
Caroline, a comfortable stay with the Goldsteins in
Hampstead, although I'm not very familiar with that part
of London, and then a somewhat dull but restful time with
Rosemary next door (lots of bridge).

I was very disappointed not to see you in London, darling.
Did you go off on holiday? Rosemary was saying how
lovely Venice was at this time of the year. She went on the
Orient Express last summer and was raving about it.

I wanted to go to the house and pay Drucilla another visit
and see more of dear Mrs Kettle. I'm so glad she has come
back. But Annabel thought it better not, for some reason.

Whatever were all those people doing there and who were
they? I sometimes think nowadays people just think they
can come and go wherever they like whenever it pleases
them.

Please be in touch soon.

Your loving mother

a pleasant weekend with Caroline

Home
London

14 June

Darling Mummy,

Thanks for your letter, for trying to pay the phone bill
(which is not working yet), for stopping the heavies from
evicting us, but mostly for being here that awful night. What
an eye-opener that was! I've been to see Claire in hospital.
She doesn't seem to know who I am, what happened or even
that she's got a daughter. The matron said they were trying
to transfer her to some kind of drying-out institution as soon
as possible.

When I've got rid of those weirdos, I'll relax. I'm aiming
to catch the 3.10 p.m. the day after tomorrow. Could you
meet me at the station?

Longing to see you.

Love,
Dru

PS: I forgot to tell you, but a vast package was delivered
here last week for Daddy from Lillywhites. It's taking
up most of the dining room. What do I do with it?

Messrs. Caper, Cures & Mine
4 Finsbury Square
London EC2

13 June

Dear Sir Anthony,

Further to your instructions, I confirm that I have completed the liquidation of your entire portfolio and arranged for the transfer of the proceeds to your numbered account with the Bank Leu in Zurich, Switzerland.

Yours sincerely,
Philip Bull

Winchester Park
Under Wallop
Hampshire

15 June

Dear Drucilla,

I wrote to your father before we left for our holiday in
Antigua, asking him and Jasmin for the Bank Holiday
weekend. I'm sorry to trouble you, dear, but could you ask
him, tactfully of course, if they are coming? I don't like
to ring as there was rather an embarrassing little scene when
they came last time and I haven't spoken to them since.
It's just that I do like to get my numbers straight in advance.
It keeps the staff happy and makes for a much more
successful group of guests.

I heard on the grapevine that your sister is back home
and having an illegitimate baby. Your poor father. What
a ghastly and dreadful responsibility for him.

It was most extraordinary but I was certain I saw your
father's double browsing at the bookstall in Antigua airport
just before we re-boarded our return flight to London. My
husband claims that I was tipsy and hallucinating. (I do
admit that I always have a little drinkie or two to calm my
nerves before flying.)

Anyway, dear, the point of this letter is to find out if they
are coming for the weekend.

Please let me know as soon as you can.

Fondest love, dear,
Fiona Hampshire

The Officers' Mess
2nd   Battalion   Scots
Guards
Falkland Islands

31 May

Dear Dru,

Just arrived in this hell-hole and wanted to 'express' this to say that I *did* come to say goodbye on Thursday evening, but I did not dare go into the house. What on earth was going on? I only hope it was not a burglary or fire.

I'll write again when we've settled in. I must say my men are all being real bricks. I feel proud to be in the British Army. Super troops!

I had to change planes in Buenos Aires and I noticed this tall distinguished looking chap propping up the airport bar, surrounded by luggage, fishing tackle, nets and so on, who looked so like your father I almost waved! Probably just feeling nostalgic at having missed you, or perhaps I'd just overdone the rum punch!

Please write.

Lots of love,
Rupert

Running Dog Rapids
Box 2242
Juneau
Alaska

25 May

Dear Primmy,

Do me a favour, dear. Ring up the Department of
Agriculture and Fisheries and ask them if one still needs forms
and licences, etc., for importing dogs into England. If so,
press them into your boy Anthony's hand.

I hope the express stamp on the envelope didn't alarm
you, dear, but it is rather urgent. I have tried telephoning
Anthony, not easy from this neck of the woods, but there
is never any reply, I wanted to catch him before he left.

Hope the dry rot has cleared up. Can't understand how
you get dry rot in such a damp climate.

In haste.

Love,
Vi

My dear Yasmin,

A few lines to say that you may be in for a disappointment
next Christmas. If you fail to understand what I am getting
at, give Dr Henderson a ring. Alas, your 'blond, blue-eyed
bundle' may not be quite what you expect. I am sorry, my
dear. No hard feelings!

Anthony